MW00628710

Copyright @ Diya Nath, 2020

ISBN: 978-1-7356711-0-9

Serapis Bey Publishing

rachnanath@gmail.com

Ordering Information: Quantity sales. Special discounts are available on quantity purchases by corporations, associations, and others. For details, contact the publisher at the address above.

Healthy Habits *for* a Healthier You

Simple, Yummy, Home-Made Smoothies to Enhance Your Gut Health and Boost Energy

Healthy Habits for a Healthier You

First Edition

By
Diya Nath

Researcher and Future Culinary Gastronomist

Dedications

Dedicated to my family.

Acknowledgements

I would like to thank my mom and dad for their continuous encouragement in documenting my work, and for their support as I met editors and publishers for the launch of this book. Thanks to my brother for tasting all my smoothies and giving positive feedback.

Thanks to all my friends and my other family members, who provided feedback on my smoothie-making and culinary skills, which further piqued my interest in publishing my work.

Thank you to Parul Agrawal for your input on my book and helping me take my book forward.

Thank you to Greg Reid and Dr. Nadia Rizzo for being instrumental in writing the foreword and also thanks to Heidi De Love for helping with the editing.

I would love to hear about your experience with smoothie making. Contact me by email at

business.diyasworld@gmail.com

Visit my website for associated materials including music that you can listen to while smoothie making as well as additional smoothie videos and resources.

You can access them at

www.diyasworld.com

You can also chat with me on https://discord.gg/pPWKRP

Or on discord @ Saki #0046 to talk about your mental wellbeing, acceptance and get support through my Program SPEAK (Support, Positivity, Equality, Acceptance/Assistance, Kindness)

Oxiblast

Order @ oxiblast.co / oxiblast.in

Table of Contents

Acknowledgements v

Foreword.. x

Introduction 1

Chapter 1: Who Am I? 4

Chapter 2: My Research on the Gut Microbiome...................... 9

Chapter 3: Main Ingredients in Your Food............................. 14

- Fats: 14
- Carbohydrates: 15
- Fruits: 17
- Vegetables: 17
- Proteins: 18
- Vitamins and Minerals: 18
- Antioxidants: 19
- Water: 20

Chapter 4: Introduction to Making Smoothies...................... 21

- What Is A Smoothie?.. 21
- Facts:... 22

Chapter 5: Introduction to Flavonoids 24

- What is Oxi-Blast®? :... 25

Chapter 6: My Journey in Picking the Best Blender............... 27

- My Experience With Blenders:.................................. 28
- Simple ways to maintain your blender quality: 29
- Parts of a blender... 30

Chapter 7: Ingredients of the Smoothie 31

- FRUITS 32
  - Apple: 32
  - Mango: 32
  - Orange: 33
  - Banana: 34
  - Pineapple: 35
  - Peaches: 36
  - Watermelon: 36
  - Cherries: 37
  - Blueberries: 38
  - Raspberries: 39
  - Strawberries: 40
  - Dates: 40

- NUTS AND SUPERFOODS 42
  - Turmeric Root: 42
  - Dark Chocolate: 43
  - Cream Cheese: 44
  - Kale: 44
  - Spinach: 45
  - Flax Seeds: 47
  - Chia Seeds: 47
  - Oxi-Blast®: 48
  - Peanut butter: 49
  - Green Tea: 49
  - Cashew: 50
  - Cinnamon: 51

Chapter 8: 21 Smoothie Recipes for a 21-Day Smoothie Challenge **52**

- 1. Tropical Citrus Boost 55
- 2. Sweet Green Machine 57
- 3. Blueberry Cheesecake 58
- 4. Strawmango Lemonade 60
- 5. Chocolate Energy 63
- 6. Dream Green 65
- 7. Banana Surprise 66
- 8. Berry Delight 68
- 9. Water Mango (My Favorite!!) 71
- 10. Almond Blueberry 73
- 11. Cherry Berry Yogurt Smoothie (Mom's Favorite!) 74
- 12. Avocado Berry Miracle 76
- 13. Citrus Green Refresher 79
- 14. Strawberry Orange Cool-Aid 81
- 15. "Potabolism" Boost 82
- 16. Banana Berry Refresher 84
- 17. Citrus Berry 87
- 18. Rose Water Green 89
- 19. Pina Colada 90
- 20. Blueberry Protein Shake 92
- 21. Strawberry and Banana Flax Smoothie 95

Chapter 9: Daily Routine for a Healthier You **96**

- 5 Tips for Storing Smoothies 97
- Sweet treats you can make from Smoothies 98
- Suggested readings 100

Glossary **105**

References **107**

Foreword

FOREWARD 1:

This is such perfect timing for this beautiful book!!! And such a perfect timing for Diya, the youth author of this magnificent, healthy volume of the yummiest recipes complete with nutritional knowledge!! We need New Leaders in the world, and here she is, raising the bar for a healthy lifestyle in every home across the Earth.

This book is important because our children (and ourselves) need help. In this world of electronics, junk food and ever-increasing stress and anxiety levels we're turning to the use of medications as stress and pain busters. Children carry medications with them and leave it at the school nurse's office like never before. Kids as young as 3-4 year olds are showing uncontrolled behavior changes, personality issues and also physical issues.

Plus, with the fast lifestyles we have, where kids are in multiple activities and sports, coming home late from daily activities, eating leftovers or quick-prep meals and then doing homework till midnight only to get up at 5 am again, we forget to take care of "US". This includes exercise, eating right and getting rid of toxins.

But with the glamorous advertisements of the "Impossible burger", juicy cheesy chicken sandwiches, potato fries and most of all Starbucks, how can you tell what's healthy and good for you? For moms and dads too exhausted to cook when they come home at 7pm and have kids and a spouse to feed, what do you do? Either get carryout or eat leftovers. This is altering your gut bacterial fauna and giving rise to diseases like Alzhemiers, Dementia, Parkinsons and other chronic diseases.

Our grandparents used to cook every day, not exercise, do all housework and still lived a healthy lifestyle; why? Is it because they were eating healthier food? Maybe, but now, due to the introduction of Genetic Engineering, many vegetables are now genetically engineered to serve the community. For example, the Flavr Savr Tomato, was genetically modified to increase shelf life, but did we even question what genetic engineering did to the other genes in the tomato? Can it be that it adversely affected the nutrient content of the fruit? We will never know. These quick fixes are causing deficiency diseases like potassium deficiency, Vit. E deficiency, Iron, calcium and the list goes on. (Simply check the USDA and FDA websites for the latest information.)

Also, along with the increase in population and agricultural lands becoming more and more rare, the nutrient content of the soil is being depleted and our daily nutrient requirement is not met even by eating double the amount of food as our grandparents did. But we don't have the time and patience to make loads of nutritious food every day. So what's the alternative?

Juicing and smoothies have been accessible to us for centuries. Many different smoothies were part of Indian, Mediterranean and even Middle Eastern cuisine for a long time. Sharbat, lassi, and other kinds of fruit blends came more into prominence after the invention of the electrical Blender in 1932 by inventor,

Stephen J. Poplawski, who received patents for a machine that would reduce fruits and vegetables to a liquid.

This book *"Healthy Habits for a Healthier You"* is a masterpiece when it comes to shedding light on the aspect of connections to food and your health. This 9th grade author, inspiring everyone to eat healthy is a revolutionary phenomenon that all the dieticians, spiritual healers, wellness coaches, scientists etc. were waiting for. Her passion in this book is scientifically based and her research on gut bacteria and its connections to health is a message that the world leaders should emphasize more. She has also started a smoothie and juicing club at school to talk about healthy eating and inspiring youth to stay healthy. Bringing awareness to this aspect in life by creating yummy, antioxidant and flavonoid rich smoothies, while keeping themselves fuller and more energetic is the intention of this young creative mind. She is conducting seminars to spread the word for connection of your gut health and the food you eat. She is also creating consciousness of a better way of eating and hence preventing problems later on.

This book also has detailed reports on the kinds of food you eat and their nutritive values, so that you can make an informed decision on what you want to eat. The chapter on the author's research is also very compelling and we know what her passion is kindled by. She also talks about flavonoids and its beneficial effects which is not known to a lot of people and her supplement of flavonoid use as an additive is genius. Look out for that supplement (Oxi-Blast®).

What I appreciate most in this book is the detail oriented yet simple way of letting people know the benefits of healthy eating and smoothie making. Most books on smoothies are just recipe books but this book goes in-depth about the choice of blenders, how to take care of them and also different ways you can preserve your smoothies for future consumption without compromising on their nutritive content. She also has a "Daily Routine for a Healthier You" section that is very beneficial and I can relate to almost all of the points she has explained in the book.

The Author is only 14 years old and so organized, so knowledgeable to have this insight of not just including smoothie recipes, but going the whole nine yards to make the audience feel comfortable with the smoothie making process too. This is very important as making smoothies is not just about blending up ingredients but for people to love the process of healthy eating and imbibe it in their lifestyles and practices as early as they can make a conscious decision.

If you know Diya personally, and her family, you will know how much a healthy lifestyle has helped her to overcome pain and disease, and you will know how much she cares for you to walk the path of health with her!! After all, people don't care as much about you unless they know how much you care, and she does. A heart of gold and a New World Leader here.

Let's go! Let's get healthy with Diya!

Greg Reid
Forbes and Inc top rated Keynote Speaker
www.GregReid.com

FOREWARD 2:

As a Naturopathic Doctor I've helped many people get on the road to a better destination with their health. A key factor in one's success on this wellness journey often comes down to one thing- how manageable the treatment plan is. Diya was given, at a relatively young age, a reality of her health that she did not want to accept, so she changed it. Her approach to healthy eating not only changed her life, it became one she chose to share for massive transformation in the lives of others. Whether nutrition is familiar to you or you feel completely lost with where to start, you need not look any further. Diya makes each step easy and simple for your everyday life, while providing easy to understand information, which can have a big impact. Above all, Diya is empowering you and showing you the way to reach your goals, just as she did for herself. Diya is giving you your power back when it comes to your health. The journey you are about to embark on with Diya is not only filled with massive transformative steps, it's filled with heart.

Dr. Nadia Rizzo ND
Author of *"Eat Your Way Sexy"*
www.nadiarizzo.com

Introduction

When Diya asked me to write the introduction for her book, I was thrilled as smoothies and nutritional eating have become my passion.My journey into healthy living started after I was introduced to the amazing world of smoothies.With my very first sip I fell in love with what I call "nutrition in a glass." I was a new mother and wanted to incorporate something healthy into my family's diet and that's when green smoothies came to my rescue. Cooking greens makes them more palatable, but we also lose about 80% of the good nutrition. However, blending greens with fruits in smoothies makes them delicious and also easy to digest still keeping the nutritional benefits intact. This was the perfect way to treat my family the healthy way. As I started researching, I found that Green Smoothies come with a huge list of benefits some of which are listed below:

More energy: Green smoothies offer pure nutrition. The amount of vitamins you'll get depends on the fruits and vegetables you choose for the smoothie. If you start the day with a green smoothie you will get all that nutrition in your system and notice a massive increase in the amount of energy you have.

Weight loss: Green smoothies are low in calories but very filling. Because they contain high amounts of water and fiber, they'll make you feel full. Green smoothies will help you with your weight loss goals by helping fight hunger and cravings.

Weight gain: If you are trying to gain weight, it is much easier to add a filling green smoothie (provided you use the right kind of vegetables) to your existing diet and drink your extra calories to put on weight.

Easy to digest: Green smoothies are easy to digest. Because they're already blended and liquefied, the body no longer needs to work so hard to "break down" the food in order to extract the nutrients. People who suffer from indigestion after eating a heavy meal will also benefit as smoothies are filling but light.

Mental clarity: Junk food, especially processed white flour and sugar, can clog our minds thus making our brains feel cloudy. Drinking green smoothies will clear your mind and make you more alert and creative.

Crave less junk: When you increase the amount of healthy foods in your diet and decrease the unhealthy foods you will naturally stop craving junk food and crave more of the same healthy food.

Improves skin; less wrinkles: Green smoothies will keep you hydrated. Although one should drink at least eight glasses of water a day, experts believe most people don't drink even half that amount. If you feel dehydrated or think you are not drinking enough water, simply add more water to the mix as you prepare your smoothie. You'll be drinking more liquids without even noticing it. The increased fluids and power of natural foods in your diet will hydrate your skin and reduce your wrinkles making you look younger. It also helps improve your immunity.

Reduce the risk of serious diseases: It is well known that one way of preventing colds, flu, allergies and even the risk of certain cancer and heart disease is to increase the number of fruit and vegetables in your diet. The more green smoothies you drink, the lower your risk.

Easy and inexpensive: Green smoothies are easy and quick to make. The only equipment you need is a blender. Home-made green smoothies are cheap. Buying smoothies at a juice bar can cost as much as $6 a glass but combining fruits and vegetables at home won't cost you more than a few cents. Drinking a glass every day will provide you with all the vitamins you need, a much cheaper (and more natural) option than buying multivitamins.

Trust me this is just a snapshot of the huge array of benefits and I am glad I found this nutritional powerhouse for my family. I wish someone had introduced me to smoothies when I was a teenager and struggling to keep up with the demands of growing years. My life and my health would have been so different had I started incorporating smoothies in my diet much earlier.

I am so happy that now we have "Healthy Habits for a Healthier You" by Diya Nath, one of the youngest proponents of smoothies. She is in true sense a health advocate for the younger generation. Her book is a perfect blend of science and art of smoothie making. It is my honor to introduce this book to you that will help you elevate your health and well-being no matter the age.

Parul Agrawal
Bestselling Author, TEDxSpeaker, Publisher
www.parulagrawal.com

Chapter 1

Who Am I?

Hi there!

My name is Diya Nath. I am a "day-after-Thanksgiving" kid born in 2005 in Mesa, Arizona. My dad, Diganta Nath, is an Engineer and works at a healthcare company with medical professionals to provide medical care to people, and my mom, Rachna Nath, is an educator, dancer, honey bee researcher and an entrepreneur. I also have a younger brother, by two years, who constantly tests my nerves by hacking into my computer, so I get back at him by making him taste and review my smoothies.

Some of my biggest passions are cooking, playing video games, drawing, singing, and listening to various genres of music. I also play the violin and love learning songs in my native language (Assamese). I also really love science and doing science experiments to learn more about the scientific world through data collection and credible experimentations.

One of my biggest passions other than cooking is hanging out with my friends; spending quality time and discussing our future trips to Michelin star restaurants all around the world. My favorite show on TV is "Tasty" and I fight with my brother every day to watch an episode of "Tasty" after dinner. Of course, I win, and he gets to sulk for 20 quick minutes.

My Health Condition:

Coming from a family background with several generations with diabetes, high blood pressure and a predisposition to certain forms of genetic diseases, it is imperative for me to stay healthy and conscious of my health.

Last year, I got all my testing done, was working with an endocrinologists and I was also declared overweight with a BMI (Body Mass Index) at 40, which falls in the Obese category (please refer to the chart below to know your BMI). The normal BMI range for my height and weight is 27-29. The doctors also said I have *Acanthosis nigricans* (darkening of skin around the neck, which is a sign of obesity or predisposition to diabetes). I was put on a diet that made me stressed about eating and I ended up gaining more weight. In spite of me being physically active, swimming and walking 10,000 steps every day, I still couldn't bring my weight down after 8 months of random dieting and exercising. I also got myself tested for the 180 food allergy IgG panel and I showed reactions to eggs, most of the pulses, rice, gluten and even to some vegetables. I was devastated and had no way to figure out how to control my weight with all my favorite food gone from the list of foods that I could relish.

I was also put on Metformin, a diabetic medication to help with my weight and my pre-diabetic condition, which I have also heard can have devastating side effects on the gut bacterial fauna, so I was determined to come up with a way to have minimal side-effects from these medications. (My two science experiments showed me enough proof that I had to take care of myself if I want to have a normal life. I explain these experiments later in another chapter.)

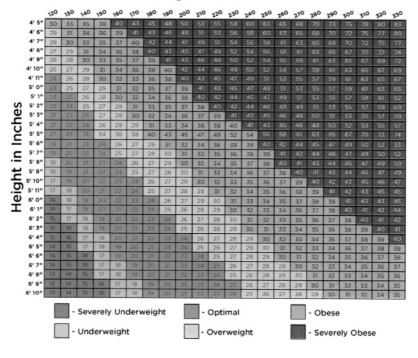

Photo from: Braceability.com

I became a Health Advocate for the younger generation:

It took me a lot of thinking and researching about *Acanthosis nigricans* and the medication that I was taking, to finally realize that a good healthy diet and a sound mindset cannot just benefit me but I can also reach out to the community in general to stay healthy and concentrate on their health. A considerable number of younger kids and students, from the age of 3 to 25 years, tend to feast on sweets, candy, sugar substitutes and snacks that are high in carbohydrates and don't maintain a healthy lifestyle. This is because of their extremely stressful schedule of study, work and even extracurricular activities. Even I remember snacking on quick McDonald burgers when I had to eat something after school and before I went to my next activity, due to lack of time.

So, the urgent question that I needed to answer was how to make these age group kids realize the importance of good habits and taking care of themselves in this fast-paced world. This has become even more necessary now during the COVID-19 situation as some kids, like me, might be at a higher risk of getting the virus and need to increase our immunity.

The best way that I found I could satisfy my hunger and also make sure my gut health was taken care of, was by introducing more and more fruits, vegetables and superfoods into my diet. Hence, I started experimenting on different smoothies and fell in love with it. I started making more and more combinations of various fruits and vegetables along with some superfood and protein sources. To my surprise, I not only satisfied my huge sweet tooth but smoothies also helped me to bring my BMI down to normal range. I also lost some weight and now I have become a huge proponent of healthy eating and hence want to spread the word and also help other kids in the process.

I am also starting a "Smoothie Making Club" at school and organizing workshops at school events to spread the word about healthy eating and the long-term benefits of maintaining one's gut health.

Visit my website, www.diyasworld.com, to learn more me and get more resources for this guide and some surprises.

Chapter 2

My Research on the Gut Microbiome

People who are predisposed to genetic conditions also need to be aware of their metabolism and control their caloric intake just like everybody else and start living healthy. I am an avid reader and with my mom's help, we try to identify problems people are facing presently because of their dietary habits and the medications they are taking. I researched a lot on how our various conditions like social anxiety, stress, and predisposed and recurrent medical conditions force us to take medications but then these medications kill our gut bacterial fauna and lead to various other secondary diseases.

According to JPND Research, scientists have shown that "changes in the composition of gut bacterial populations...are actively contributing to...the deterioration of motor skills." This research also says that the deterioration of motor skills is the biggest sign of Parkinson's disease (PD). In a ScienceNews Report, "Parkinson's Pathways", it is said that people with PD have more digestive issues as well as diarrhea or constipation, bloating, nausea and other gastrointestinal issues (McNamara). Bauer also writes that imbalances and stress of the gut bacteria in the gut microbiome are the cause of many GI (gastrointestinal) issues and many infections and diseases.

Neurodegenerative diseases are another issue that affect the neurons in the brain or peripheral nervous system that ultimately die due to gradual or sudden loss of function. Neurons are the primary component of the brain and the spinal cord and form our nervous system. The neurons however, unlike the other cells in our body, don't regenerate and cannot be replaced by our body. Sadly, neurodegenerative diseases are incurable and extremely debilitating and could have incredibly negative effects on someone. About 60,000 Americans are diagnosed with Parkinson's disease every year (Parkinson's News Today). According to NIH (National Institute of Health), an estimated 5.4 million Americans currently have Alzheimer's and an estimated 93 thousand and over will get Parkinson's by 2020.

With an increase of Neurodegenerative diseases like Alzheimer's, Parkinson's, Frontotemporal lobar degeneration, dementia, Huntington's, spinocerebellar ataxia, etc. the question that comes to mind is, Is there a common pathway for the occurrence of these neuronal diseases? Most of these are now being referred to as "GUT DISEASES" and not Neurological ones as they are believed to originate in the gut due to the gut bacterial fauna change.

According to Walker et.al, all of these diseases have a misfolded protein with amyloid polymer (sticky long molecule) structure that behaves like a Prion (infectious proteins), and is related to sterile cerebral (front part of the brain) inflammation. Although the misfolded proteins for all of the above-mentioned diseases are different, the biophysical properties of the aggregates are conserved (Walker, 2016). Scientists have recognized that the need to understand these diseases better is of utmost importance and that both genetic and environmental conditions have a role in contributing to the development of these diseases.

To understand these conditions better, I performed two science experiments that gave me a clearer perspective and reinforced my belief in the importance of healthy eating and maintaining gut health.

Experiment 1:

Last year, I used *1 mm transparent worms called C. elegans* to study their changes in body length when they are exposed to different medications that people take on a daily basis, because of different medical problems like diabetes and high blood pressure. The body length showed differences in expression of a specific gene that increases metabolism and hence changes body length of the *C. elegans in response to these medications.* This is direct evidence of our diet and habits influencing our physiology. This work will be published soon.

Experiment 2:

The health of the gut microbiome is also good for overall body health. Bauer also writes that "a balanced gut microbiota creates a symbiotic relationship that benefits the host and the resident microbes." Rich diversity of gut bacteria is essential to better health. Unfamiliar foods help with providing nutrition for many types of bacteria, and then the bacteria "produce compounds that help maintain human health." He also writes that by strengthening the gut lining and helping the immune system regulate inflammation, the gut influences human health. This evidence clearly shows that the health of the gut microbiota is very important to better overall health.

Medical News Today states that "Diabetes is a condition that impairs the body's ability to process blood glucose, otherwise known as blood sugar." My mom has hypertension (high blood pressure) and takes amlodipine, and my dad has type 2 diabetes and takes losartan and metformin to manage his diabetes. These medicines along with common painkillers, Ibuprofen and Tylenol, and nicotine concentrations 0.3 and 0.6% were tested on the growth and stress of the *E. coli* bacteria. The results showed that the bacteria become stressed when their environmental conditions change or fluctuate. Their process of cell division was not carried out properly and instead of breaking apart, the bacterium grows longer and longer and forms filaments (called Curli in medical terminologies). These filaments in the future lead to the formation of plaque that might travel up to the brain via different pathways to cause neurological diseases. My results showed that the bacteria didn't even grow in some petri dishes with medication suggesting that those medications are bad for gut health. But important was the finding of stressed curli bacteria in ibuprofen, losartan, metformin and also amlodipine culture plates. This showed that the medications people are taking are causing changes in their gut bacteria.

Gut *E. coli* and Stress

Normal E.coli in the gut

Stressed out E.coli in the gut forming filaments

E. coli bacteria that is normal and stressed under medications. The orange arrows show the filament formation of the bacteria that are presumed to cause plaque and hence neurological problems.

Hence, our dietary habits become an essential part of our way of life that helps to keep our gut bacterial fauna intact and also prevents different other diseases. According to Harvard School of Public Health, some ways to decrease your risk of type 2 diabetes are controlling weight, staying active, avoiding and decreasing smoking and alcohol consumption, and maintaining a balanced diet.

Everyday Health writes that maintaining a healthy weight, diet, regular activity, cutting back on salt and limiting alcohol consumption can decrease your risk of hypertension. So, what is the easiest and quickest way to make a healthy change? How do we know what to eat? How much to eat and when? What products are good for us and what foods should we avoid? Let's find out together.

Chapter 3

Main Ingredients in Your Food

In the previous chapter, I talked about my science experiment and how it was related to preventing diabetes and hypertension and keeping the gut microbiome healthy. These two diseases require huge lifestyle changes, as well as maintaining a healthy diet. Many of you are wondering how your diet impacts you, what your diet should have, and why smoothies are so good to include into your diet. According to the National Heart, Lung, and Blood Institute, a healthy diet includes emphasis on fruits, vegetables and whole grains. Limitation of foods from concentrate, added sugars and trans fats are also key for a healthy diet. Let's look at the different kind of foods that we eat on a daily basis:

FATS:

First, healthy fats are essential to any diet. The American Heart Association states that "dietary fats are essential to give your body energy and to support cell growth." Not only do they insulate your organs and keep your body warm, they also help your body absorb some nutrients. There are 2 main types of fats:

- ❖ Saturated
- ❖ Unsaturated

Saturated fats tend to be solid at room temperature. Some saturated fats include butter, lard, coconut oil, and cocoa butter and that found in foods like dark poultry. Unsaturated fats are usually liquids at room temperature. Some unsaturated fats are olive, avocado, nuts, nut butters and that found in some fish (salmon, mackerel). Trans fats are a type of saturated fat and should be avoided because they raise LDL cholesterol levels, or bad cholesterol levels.

 Overall, healthy fats are essential for the body's energy sources and have a large number of benefits.

CARBOHYDRATES:

Carbs or carbohydrates are essential for the body. HealthLine states that carbohydrates provide the body with energy and stored energy. When carbohydrates are digested, they are broken down into glucose and are used to make ATP or adenosine triphosphate, which provides energy to the body.

Carbohydrates are also good for maintaining muscle mass. HealthLine reports that when a person is lacking glucose from carbohydrates in unideal scenarios, their body is able to break down muscle mass into amino acids and then can be converted into glucose for ATP. <u>One way to prevent or improve this is to include a good amount of carbs into your diet because they provide your body with the glucose it needs to make ATP.</u>

Whole grains are also essential to your diet because of their numerous health benefits. There are 3 parts to a whole grain, the bran, the endosperm and the germ.

- ❖ The bran is the hard, outer shell which contains antioxidants, fiber and minerals.
- ❖ The endosperm is the middle layer which is mostly carbs.
- ❖ The germ is the inner layer which contains minerals and protein. (Jennings).

Some common whole grains include oats, millet, brown rice, buckwheat barley, bulgur and quinoa. Whole grains are high in fiber, protein, antioxidants and minerals which are nutrients necessary for your body's health. They can also decrease your risk of many diseases including heart disease, cancer, type 2 diabetes and can support digestive health. Therefore, whole grains are necessary because they provide tons of nutrients that are key to achieving a healthy lifestyle.

 Whole grains are very beneficial for the body because they can lower the risk of many diseases. Overall, carbohydrates are essential because they provide glucose for the body to make ATP/energy.

FRUITS:

Next, fruits are incredibly beneficial for your body's health. According to Healthline, fruits have numerous benefits such as fiber, folate, vitamins, antioxidants, omega-3, fatty acids, etc. Oranges, red peppers and strawberries are rich in vit-C, and oranges, mangoes and other tropical fruits are high in folate, which are awesome for fetal development (for pregnancy) and help with red blood cell production. Bananas, guavas and mangoes are high in potassium, which maintains good blood pressure. For these reasons, it is absolutely imperative that a variety of fruits are included into your diet.

 The AHA (American Heart Association) recommends about 5 servings of fruit a day.

VEGETABLES:

Next, vegetables have a huge number of benefits that you don't want to miss out on. USDA ChooseMyPlate says that "eating a diet of vegetables and fruits…may reduce risk for heart disease, including heart attack and stroke." It can also prevent different types of cancers, obesity and type2 diabetes. Vegetables also have tons of potassium, dietary fiber, folate and vitamins which can lead to a healthier diet overall and are vital for your body's maintenance and health.

 The USDA recommends 5-9 servings of fruits and vegetables per day for the average adult.

PROTEINS:

Proteins are a must for people who are trying to incorporate healthier foods into their diet. Detourbar reports that some good reasons that protein should be in your diet are:

- ❖ They make up many essential parts of your body including your skin, hair and nails. They are also used to make enzymes, hormones and body chemicals.
- ❖ They help repair and build tissue.
- ❖ They are also essential for bone, muscle, cartilage, blood and skin structure.
- ❖ They help maintain a healthy weight and reduce muscle loss.
- ❖ They help speed up recovery after workouts and curb hunger.

 Proteins are the most plentiful substance in the body.

VITAMINS AND MINERALS:

Getting the right amounts of vitamins and minerals into your body is very important because they perform hundreds of functions. "They help shore up bones, heal wounds and bolster your immune system. They also convert food into energy and repair cellular damage." (HelpGuide). Some benefits of vitamins and minerals include:

- ❖ Make for healthy, strong bones and teeth, and help heal bones.
- ❖ Strengthen immune system thereby helping reduce risk of disease.

❖ Improve eye, gut, and body health.According to Reader's Digest, the 13 necessary vitamins the body needs are "vitamins A, C, D, E, K and the B vitamins: thiamine (B1), riboflavin (B2), niacin (B3), pantothenic acid (B5), pyridoxine (B6), biotin (B7), folate (B9) and cobalamin (B12)." Vitamins are incredibly important to include in your diet and will help you tremendously in the path to eating healthy.

 You can easily get too many nutrients from vitamins, which can harm you, so always check with your physician when taking supplements (HelpGuide).

ANTIOXIDANTS:

Antioxidants are a requirement in a healthy diet. According to Mayo Clinic, antioxidants <u>help protect your cells against damage caused by free radicals</u>. Free radicals are unstable molecules that are created when molecules gain or lose electrons, when the body is exposed to tobacco or radiation. Some types of antioxidants include flavonoids, phenols, tannins and lignans. Some great sources for antioxidants are:

❖ Plant-based foods
❖ Fruits and vegetables
❖ Whole grains
❖ Nuts and seeds
❖ Cocoa

 One of the largest sources of antioxidants is coffee. The total amount of antioxidants in coffee overtakes the amount in berries. Hence it is recommended by experts to have coffee in moderation.

WATER:

When doing a cleanse or diet, it is always important to drink lots of water. Water makes more of an impact on your diet than you think. Our body is made up of 70% water. Usually, about 8 glasses of water is recommended per day. According to Health-Line: "7 Science-Based Health Benefits of Drinking Enough Water," some huge benefits of water are:

- ❖ Maximizes physical performance
- ❖ Has major effect on energy levels and brain function
- ❖ Can prevent and treat headaches and relieve constipation
- ❖ Can help treat kidney stones and also help prevent hangovers
- ❖ Drinking more water can help with weight loss and can help flush out toxins

 Nearly 70% of the brain is water (Seametrics).

Having learnt the benefits of different varieties of food, in the next chapter, let's talk about why you should incorporate smoothies into your diet to get all of these necessary nutrients.

Chapter 4

Introduction to Making Smoothies

If you came this far, I assume you are convinced that having a balanced diet is essential and that smoothies with the right ingredients are incredibly nutritious. I also assume that you want to learn a bit more about smoothies! In the previous chapter, I talked about what a good diet should have, the benefits from having a good diet, and then briefly talked about why smoothies are great to implement into a balanced diet. Now, I will go into more detail on smoothies.

WHAT IS A SMOOTHIE?

First, a smoothie is a blended drink with usually:

1. Liquid base (water, half and half of any kind of milk, tea, or coconut water)
2. Fruits (fresh preferred if possible)

3. Veggies (greens like kale, lettuce, swiss chard, spinach and other veggies like carrots, sweet potato, cauliflower, etc.)
4. Some kind of protein (nut butters, beans, yogurt, tofu, nuts, avocado or protein powder)
5. Superfoods (chia seeds, hemp seeds, goji berries, flax seeds, acai, cacao and spirulina)

FACTS:

1. **Flax seeds are high in omega-3 fatty acids and fiber and increase good cholesterol levels.**
2. **Hemp seeds are rich in healthy fats and fatty acids, protein, vitamins and minerals (HealthLine).**
3. **Goji berries provide immune system support, protect the eye, stabilize blood sugar and improve anxiety, depression and sleep.**
4. **Chia seeds have omega-3 fatty acids, fiber, calcium and antioxidants (medicalnewstoday).**
5. **Acai is incredibly rich in antioxidants and fiber (Mayo Clinic).**
6. **Cacao are filled with antioxidants, magnesium, iron and calcium (begoodorganics).**
7. **Spirulina is incredibly rich in antioxidants, can reduce blood pressure, can protect against anemia, and even has anti-inflammatory properties (HealthLine).**

Chia Seeds, Flax Meal and Oxi-Blast

Chapter 5

Introduction to Flavonoids

How many of you throw away the fruit and vegetable peel used in juicing, making smoothies or even cooking? Why do you think the peels make a good compost?

Do you know they contain beneficial Flavonoids?

Flavonoids are plant products that are produced through secondary metabolic pathways. (Healthline). There are 6 types of flavonoids:

1. **Flavonols:** Known for their antioxidant properties, found in onions, kale, grapes, tea, peaches, berries, tomatoes, etc.
2. **Flavan-3-ols:** Known for their nutrient rich content, found in cocoa and its products, different kinds of tea, purple and red grapes, blueberries and strawberries.
3. **Flavones:** Act as natural pesticides and reduce inflammation and found in blue and white flowering plants like peppermint, celery, red peppers, chamomile, parsley etc.

4. **Flavanones:** These are anti-inflammatory and help in maintaining weight and cholesterol. Found in lemons, limes, grapefruits, and oranges.
5. **Isoflavones:** They keep the hormones in balance and are found in fava beans, soy and soy products and also in certain legumes.
6. **Anthocyanins:** Found in the outer skin of the berries, they are antioxidants.

What is Oxi-Blast®? :

I have started a new product line called "Oxi-Blast", (coming to market soon), that is a combination of different flavonoids that you can use as a superfood and add it to any smoothie you want for added benefits. Some of my favorite Oxi-Blast additives are from apples, oranges, pomegranates, mangoes, banana, tomatoes, oranges, bitter gourd, different kinds of squashes, lemons, zucchini and even the greens on the strawberries. More details on Oxi-Blast and their individual benefits to come in the second edition.

Orange, apple, and banana additives, a source of quick superfood.

This is an awesome superfood because peels are incredibly high in nutrients. HealthLine reports that "a raw apple with skin contains up to 332% more vitamin K, 142% more vitamin A, 115% more vitamin C, 20% more calcium and up to 19% more potassium than a peeled apple." Also, it states that the skin on vegetables has "31% of the total amount of fiber." In fruits, the peels have about 328 times the amount of antioxidants than the pulp. Peels also help you feel fuller for a longer period of time and can help lower your risk of disease. They also reported that peeling a peach (in a study) resulted in a 13-48% reduction in antioxidants, which is a nutrient vital for protecting our body against high free-radical levels. Overall, fruit peels contain a large chunk of the fruit or vegetable's nutrients, which is why I believe fruit peels are an important superfood. All the free radicals produced as a result of daily activities can be counteracted by eating healthy and also by adding Oxi-Blast to your smoothies along with flax seeds, chia seeds and omega-3 fatty acids.

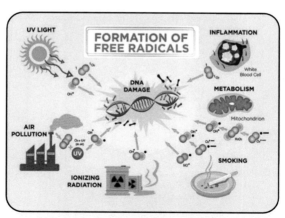

Figure shows how free radicals that harm our body are formed. (Solesence.com). Antioxidants help reduce free radicals and prevent DNA damage.

Chapter 6

My Journey in Picking the Best Blender

Blenders are required for making smoothies. A blender consists of a blender jar with a rotating metal blade and is powered by an electric motor in the base. The strength and quality of your blender decides how smooth or chunky your smoothie comes out. There are a variety of blenders to choose from. Some common blender brands include:

- Magic Bullet
- NutriBullet
- Nutri Ninja
- Vitamix
- Blendtec
- Harley Pasternak
- Breville
- Hamilton Beach
- Oster
- Cuisinart

I have used Cuisinart, Magic Bullet, NutriBullet, Harley Pasternak Power Blender, and Oster.

MY EXPERIENCE WITH BLENDERS:

In my smoothies, I look for no chunks of fruit, nut or vegetable. I also like smoothies on the thicker side, so I use ice and/or frozen fruit and less liquid in my smoothies. This is why, out of all the blenders I have used, **Harley Pasternak is the best one for making sure no chunks are in my smoothies.** The Harley Pasternak Power Blender is a 1500-watt blender with a 5 year warranty and performed well in terms of a blender test program at Consumer Reports (Consumer Reports). The blender was proven to be of high-quality and very versatile.

Now, speaking from experience, my least favorite blender, by far, has been the Magic Bullet. The quality diminished with every use of it. After a while of using it, liquid poured outside of the blender itself and it wasn't even able to blend bananas. On the other hand, NutriBullet did not have the same problem. It had decent strength and warranty. Oster and Cuisinart also were pretty decent, but it took a long period of blending to get the right consistency. I prefer Oster over Cuisinart because it has a low and high setting and offers different blending modes like smoothie, milkshake, frozen dessert, etc. Some high-quality blenders that people have talked about on social media are Vitamix, Blendtec and Nutri Ninja. These blenders are high-speed blenders each with special features like different blade shape, timers, tampers, etc. I recommend the Harley Pasternak or one of these high-speed blenders for achieving the texture you want for your smoothies.

Brand	Vitamix	Vitamix	Blendtec	Cleanblend	Dash	Ninja	Ninja	Ninja	Ninja	KitchenAid
Model	Professional Series 300	5300	Designer Series Blender	Commercial Blender	Chef Series Digital Blender	BL642	BL610	BL580	QB1004	KSB1570
Watts	1656	1640	1560	1800	1400	1200	1000	1100	450	670
Speeds	10	10	8	10	16	5	3	2	1	5
Pulse	Yes	Yes	Yes	Yes	Yes	Yes	Yes	Yes	No	Yes
Smoothie Grade	A	A	A	A	A	A-	B	B+	B	C
Ice Crush Grade	A	A	A	A	B	B	A	B	B	B
Puree Grade	A	A	A	B	A	B	B	B	C	B
Jar Material	BPA-Free Plastic	BPA-Free Plastic	BPA-Free Tritan	BPA-Free Plastic	BPA-Free Tritan	BPA-Free Plastic	BPA-Free Plastic	BPA-Free Plastic	Plastic	BPA-Free Plastic
Capacity (Ounces)	64 oz	64 oz	90 oz / 36 oz blending capacity	64 oz	64 oz	72 oz, 32 oz, 24 oz, or 18 oz	72 oz	24 oz	48 oz	56 oz
Controls	Dial and toggle	Dial and toggle	Touchscreen controls	Dial and toggle	Dial and Digital touchpad; 6 Presets	Touchpad	Touchpad	Touchpad	Push Down	Touchpad
Dimensions (H x W x D)	18" x 8" x 9"	18" x 8" x 9"	15" x 9.25" x 7"	21" x 8" x 9"	22" x 9" x 10"	18" x 7" x 10"	15.75" x 10.6" x 8.2"	15.9" x 6.3" x 6.7"	14" x 9" x 6"	15.2" x 8.6" x 9"
Warranty	7 years	7 years	8 years	5 years	1 year Parts, 7 years Motor	1 year	1 year	1 year	1 year	1 year
Price	$429.99	$379.00	$408.98	$198.97	$199.98	$147.19	$67.27	$89.00	$45.09	$79.00
Relevant Rankings Rating	9.3	9.4	9.3	6.2	9.2	9.1	9	9	8.7	8.4

Comparison of blenders available in the market. Adopted from Blender Comparison Chart 2019-ISSUU

Simple ways to maintain your blender quality:

1. While using the blender, make sure that the juicer fits perfectly into the base.
2. To avoid jamming of the blender, cut food into smaller pieces and add some liquid to it.
3. Clean the blender immediately after use every time. If you wait to clean, the food becomes dried up and sticks to the side of the blender.
4. After use, fill the jar with water halfway, add a drop of detergent and blend at low speed. After that, clear water should be used to rinse it and the base should be cleaned with a damp sponge.
5. You can make your own detergent by adding 3 spoonfuls' of vinegar, 2 tbsp of lemon juice and 1 cup of water.

6. Never use running water or immerse the jar in water.
7. After you are done blending and washing, unplug the blender and remove the blade assembly by unscrewing the jar base. This should be done at least once every two weeks to keep the blender running smoothly.
8. Wash the blade assembly with detergent and rinse.
9. If a leak occurs, remove the blade immediately and check for cracks in the jar or in the ring. Replace whatever is needed.
10. Sometimes the entire blade assembly might need to be replaced.
11. Read the instruction manual before the first use.

Parts of a blender

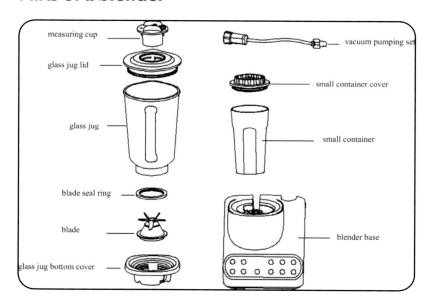

Figure showing parts of a Krogan 1300 Rapid Blender (Krogan .com)

Chapter 7

Ingredients of the Smoothie

"The fridge had been emptied of all Dudley's favorite things — fizzy drinks and cakes, chocolate bars and burgers — and filled instead with fruit and vegetables and the sorts of things that Uncle Vernon called 'rabbit food'."

~ J. K. Rowling

FRUITS

Apple:

Apples are great to include into your diet because they have low sugar content and a high fiber and Vitamin C content.

Nutrition of one medium apple:

- ❖ 100 calories
- ❖ 25 grams of carbohydrates
- ❖ 4 grams of fiber
- ❖ 19 grams of sugar
- ❖ A variety of strong antioxidants

Apples are also very high in flavonoids. They have pectin, a fiber that breaks down in your gut. Lots of the fiber and flavonoids are in the apple peels, so it is lost when people peel the apples. The fiber can slow digestion so you feel fuller after eating. This can keep you from overeating. Eating fiber-rich foods helps control symptoms and lessens acid reflux effects. "An apple's fiber can also help with diarrhea and constipation." (WebMd).

 Apples are very strong antioxidants and have high sources of Vitamin C

Mango:

Mango is low in calories yet high in Vitamin C, which aids immunity, iron absorption and growth and repair. Mango also has high polyphenol content, which is a type of antioxidant that can protect body tissues against oxidative stress and infection (NCBI). Antioxidants are important as they protect your cells against free-radical damage. Free radicals are highly reactive compounds that can bind to and damage your cells. According to USDA, one cup (165 grams) of mango provides 10% of your daily vitamin A needs.

 One cup (165 grams) of sliced mango provides (2 Trusted Source) 18% Folate, 67% Vitamin C of Reference Daily Intake (RDI), 6% Potassium and 99 calories.

Orange:

Oranges are incredibly high in Vitamin C, plant compounds and antioxidants that can work against disease and can reduce inflammation. Vitamin C can protect cells against damage done by free radicals.

Nutritional value of a medium orange:

❖ 45 calories
❖ 0.16 g of fat
❖ 237 milligrams of potassium

❖ 15.4 g of carbohydrate
❖ 12.2 g of sugar
❖ 1.23 g of protein

 There are over 600 different varieties of oranges worldwide; they spread from South West Asia in the early 4000 B.C

Banana:

Bananas are a must in any type of diet. They are high in Vitamin B6, C, potassium and manganese. Vitamin B6 helps "produce red blood cells, metabolize carbohydrates and fats, turning them into energy, metabolize amino acids, remove unwanted chemicals from your liver and kidneys, and maintain a healthy nervous system." "Manganese helps your body make collagen and protects your skin and other cell against free-radical damage. Potassium helps your body maintain a healthy heart and blood pressure. In addition, bananas are low in sodium." (6 Good Reasons to Eat a Banana Today).

 In 327 BC, when Alexander the Great and his army invaded India, he discovered the banana crop in the Indian Valleys. After tasting this unusual fruit for the first time, he introduced this new discovery to the Western world. Bananas are the most popular fruit in the world; in fact, over 100 billion bananas are eaten around the world every year, and around 51% of these are eaten at breakfast time.

Pineapple:

Pineapples are extremely important and are a popular fruit. Pineapples contain trace amounts of vitamins A and K, phosphorus, zinc and calcium but are especially rich in Vitamin C, manganese and flavonoids. Vitamin C is essential for growth and development and a healthy immune system. Meanwhile, manganese helps with growth, helps maintain a healthy metabolism and has antioxidant properties (8 Impressive Health Benefits of Pineapple).

 Pineapples contain the Bromelain enzyme that is used to tenderize meat.

Peaches:

Peaches are packed with antioxidants, fiber, vitamins and minerals. They can also help with improving heart and skin health, improve digestion and can help prevent different types of cancer. They can also help relieve allergy symptoms, boost immunity, can protect against certain toxins, and can even reduce blood sugar levels (10 Surprising Health Benefits and Uses of Peaches).

 The health benefits of peach fruit include relief from hypokalemia, cancer, obesity, cholesterol, blood stasis and neurodegenerative diseases.

Watermelon:

Watermelon is an incredible fruit to eat because it is so rich in nutrients and is hydrating. It is high in Vitamin C and A and is only 46 calories per one cup.

This is the nutritional content in one cup of watermelon:

* ❖ Vitamin C: 21% of the Reference Daily Intake (RDI)
* ❖ Vitamin A: 18% of the RDI
* ❖ Potassium: 5% of the RDI
* ❖ Magnesium: 4% of the RDI
* ❖ Vitamins B1, B5 and B6: 3% of the RDI

Watermelon is also able to help prevent cancer, improve heart health, lower inflammation and oxidative stress, help prevent macular degeneration (degeneration of the central area of the retina, which can affect your eyesight), relieve muscle soreness, improve digestion, and also helps with maintaining good skin and hair health (Top 9 Health Benefits of Eating Watermelon).

 The word "watermelon" first appeared in the English dictionary in 1615. The heaviest watermelon weighed 159 kg (350.5 lb) and was grown by Chris Kent (USA) of Sevierville, Tennessee, USA, as verified by the Great Pumpkin Commonwealth on 4 October 2013.

Cherries:

Cherries are tasty, nutritious, and popular fruits. They are also packed with vitamins, minerals and fiber.

This is the nutritional content of 1 cup of raw cherries:

- ❖ Calories: 97
- ❖ Protein: 2 grams
- ❖ Carbs: 25 grams
- ❖ Fiber: 3 grams
- ❖ Vitamin C: 18% of the RDI
- ❖ Potassium: 10% of the RDI
- ❖ Copper: 5% of the RDI
- ❖ Manganese: 5% of the RDI

Cherries are rich in polyphenols, which can help fight cellular damage, reduce inflammation, and promote overall health. Cherries are also rich in Vitamin C, which has anti-inflammatory and antioxidant properties. Some other benefits of cherries include boosting exercise recovery, benefitting heart health, improving arthritis and gout symptoms, and can improve sleep quality (7 Impressive Health Benefits of Cherries).

 One review found that eating cherries effectively reduced inflammation in 11 out of 16 studies and markers of oxidative stress in 8 out of 10 studies (HealthLine).

Blueberries:

Blueberries are a low-sugar fruit packed with nutrients and have a number of health benefits. This is the nutritional value in 1 cup of blueberries:

* Fiber: 4 grams
* Vitamin C: 24% of the RDI (Reference Daily Intake)
* Vitamin K: 36% of the RDI
* Manganese: 25% of the RDI

Blueberries are extremely high in antioxidant content. Some other benefits of blueberries include reducing DNA damage (which can help reduce risk of cancer and aging), protecting cholesterol from damage, lowering blood pressure, helping prevent heart disease, improving brain function and they can help fight urinary tract infections and many more (10 Proven Health Benefits of Blueberries).

 Blueberry reports that blueberries were ranked #1 in having antioxidant health benefits compared to 40 other fruits and vegetables.

Raspberries:

Raspberries are berries incredibly rich in Vitamin C, fiber, antioxidants and tons of other nutrients. Other benefits include preventing diseases (with powerful antioxidants), helping control blood pressure, potentially aiding in weight loss, helping improve arthritis, and can combat aging and much more. Varieties of raspberries include purple, black, golden and red raspberries.

This is the nutritional value in 1 cup of raspberries:

- Calories: 64
- Carbs: 14.7 grams
- Protein: 1.5 grams
- Fat: 0.8 grams
- Vitamin C: 54% of the Reference Daily Intake (RDI)
- Manganese: 41% of the RDI
- Vitamin K: 12% of the RDI
- Vitamin E: 5% of the RDI
- Iron: 5% of the RDI
- Magnesium: 7% of the RDI
- Phosphorus: 4% of the RDI

 There are over 200 different species of raspberries, but only 2 are being grown on a large scale.

Strawberries:

Strawberries are incredible berries to include into our diet. They have a large content of Vitamin C, manganese, folate and potassium. Strawberries also have a low glycemic index of 40.

This is the nutritional value of 3.5 ounces of strawberries:

❖ Carbs: 7.7 grams
❖ Sugar: 4.9 grams

❖ Fiber: 2 grams
❖ Fat: 0.3 grams

Strawberries are also incredibly versatile. They can be eaten raw, cooked, in desserts, jams, smoothies, juices, etc. Some other benefits of strawberries include improved heart health, regulating blood sugar and they help with cancer prevention (Strawberries 101: Nutrition Facts and Health Benefits).

 Strawberries are among the top 20 fruits in antioxidant capacity and are a good source of manganese and potassium.

Dates:

Dates are extremely rich in nutrients, more than other fruits because they are dried.

These are the nutrients in 3.5 oz of dates:

❖ Potassium: 20% of the RDI
❖ Magnesium: 14% of the RDI
❖ Copper: 18% of the RDI

- ❖ Manganese: 15% of the RDI
- ❖ Iron: 5% of the RDI
- ❖ Vitamin B6: 12% of the RDI

Dates are also high in antioxidants, which help reduce cell damage from free radicals. Also, in a study, dates were found to promote brain health because they are helpful in lowering inflammatory markers and reducing amyloid-beta proteins which can form plaques in the brain (Eliott).

 Dates have been proven to promote and ease late-term labor in pregnant women.

Turmeric Root:

Scientists now believe that chronic, low-level inflammation plays a major role in almost every chronic, Western disease. This includes heart disease, cancer, metabolic syndrome, Alzheimer's and various degenerative conditions. Curcumin, the main ingredient of Turmeric roots, is strongly anti-inflammatory, antioxidant, and lowers the chances of heart diseases. It is also good for Arthritis.

One tablespoon serving provides:

- ❖ 26 percent of daily manganese needs
- ❖ 16 percent of daily iron
- ❖ 5 percent of daily potassium
- ❖ 3 percent of daily Vitamin C

 Curcumin is poorly absorbed into the blood-stream. It helps to consume black pepper with it, which contains piperine, a natural substance that enhances the absorption of curcumin by 2,000%.

Dark Chocolate:

Dark chocolate with at least 60% cocoa is incredibly nutritious. It is full of antioxidants and help with improving blood flow and decreasing blood pressure. Dark chocolate also helps with raising HDL and protects LDL from oxidation, which means that the LDL has reacted with free radicals. Again, free radicals are substances that can deal damage to cells, so this is incredibly important (Gunnars).

USDA says that a 101-gram bar of chocolate contains:

- ❖ 11.00 grams of dietary fiber
- ❖ 24.23 grams of sugar
- ❖ 12.02 milligrams of iron
- ❖ 230.00 milligrams of magnesium
- ❖ 3.34 milligrams of zinc

 A study showed that eating high-flavanol cocoa helped improve blood flow to the brain (Gunnars).

Cream Cheese:

Cream Cheese is nothing but cheese with FDA describing it as 33% fat with 55% or less moisture content. This cheese is similar to mascarpone cheese. Once lactic acid is added to the cheese, the pH of the cheese decreases causing separation of whey and curd and after the separation of whey, cream cheese is formed. It is a good source of Vitamin A and Riboflavin (Vitamin B2).

In general, 1 ounce (28 grams) of regular cream cheese provides:

* Calories: 99
* Protein: 2 grams
* Fat: 10 grams
* Vitamin A: 10% of the Daily Value (DV)
* Riboflavin (vitamin B2): 5% of the DV

 Cream Cheese came into popularity in the late 1800s and was produced mostly in Philadelphia— of course! While developed in the States, it is consumed globally these days.

Kale:

Kale is an awesome green vegetable that is rich in vitamins and minerals. A single cup of raw kale (about 67 grams or 2.4 ounces) contains:

* Vitamin A: 206% of the RDI (from beta-carotene)
* Vitamin K: 684% of the RDI
* Vitamin C: 134% of the RDI

- Vitamin B6: 9% of the RDI
- It also contains 3% or more of the RDI for vitamin B1 (thiamin), vitamin B2 (riboflavin), vitamin B3 (niacin), iron and phosphorus

One cup also includes a total of 33 calories, 6 grams of carbs (2 of which are fiber) and 3 grams of protein.

Kale contains very little fat, but a large portion of the fat in it is an omega-3 fatty acid called alpha linolenic-acid, which is essential for normal growth and development (10 Health Benefits of Kale).

Given its incredibly low calorie content, kale is among the most rewarding foods in existence. Eating more kale is a great way to get the total nutrient content of your diet.

Spinach:

Spinach is an excellent green vegetable to include into your diet. It is a great source of vitamin K, vitamin A (in the form of carotenoids), manganese, folate, magnesium, iron, copper, vitamin B2, vitamin B6, vitamin E, calcium, potassium, Vitamin C and so much more.

The health benefits of spinach include skin care, improved eyesight, stronger bones, stronger muscles, regulated blood pressure, preventing or managing diabetes, good for your heart, anti-cancerous benefits and prevention of age-related macular degeneration (AMD) and hemophilia (WebMD).

One cup of spinach contains:

❖ 30 milligrams (mg) of calcium2,813 international units (IU) of Vitamin A58 micrograms of folate

 According to the USDA, on average, each American eats 1.4 kilograms (3 pounds) of spinach a year: 0.9 kilogram (2 pounds) of fresh spinach and 1 pound (0.45 kilograms) of processed spinach.

Flax Seeds:

Flax seeds are great to include in your diet and have a huge number of health benefits too good to miss out on.

This is the nutritional value of 1 tablespoon of flax seeds:

- ❖ Vitamin B1: 8% of the RDI (Reference Daily Intake)
- ❖ Vitamin B6: 2% of the RDI
- ❖ Folate: 2% of the RDI
- ❖ Calcium: 2% of the RDI
- ❖ Potassium: 2% of the RDI

Flax seeds also have a large content of omega-3 fatty acids, which are great for lowering your risk of heart disease and heart problems and lowering blood pressure. They are also rich in lignans, which can reduce the risk of cancer, improve cholesterol, control hunger and contribute to weight loss (Top 10 Health Benefits of Flax Seeds).

 Flaxseeds make you go regularly because they are super crazy high in fiber.

Chia Seeds:

Chia seeds are a common food for people to include in smoothies and into their diet. They are a rich source in omega-3 fatty acids, fiber, and vitamins and minerals.

This is the nutritional value of an ounce of chia seeds:

❖ Protein: 4 gramsCalcium: 18% of the RDI (Reference Daily Intake)Manganese: 30% of the RDIMagnesium: 30% of the RDIPhosphorus: 27% of the RDI Some other benefits of chia seeds include high-quality protein content and fiber content, help with weight loss, reduced risk of heart disease, high in nutrients needed for bone strength, reducing blood sugar levels and reducing chronic inflammation.

 Chia seeds can also be used as aface mask and used for skin hydration, too.

Oxi-Blast®:

Fruit peels have flavonoids that have huge health benefits. Banana peels have serotonin, apple peels have procyanidins, catechin, epicatechin, chlorogenic acid, phloridzin and quercetin, orange peels have the highest content of polymethoxylated flavones, mango peels have catechin, epicatechin, quercetin, isoquercetin (quercetin-3-glucoside), fisetin and astragalin (kaempferol-3-glucoside). These are all antioxidants and have anti-inflammatory properties and are exceptionally beneficial to people. A new product is coming out soon with all the benefits of these peels. Look out for it.

 Oxi-Blast is antioxidants and flavonoids that help keep you healthy.

Peanut butter:

Peanut butter is a great source of nutrients and is an awesome option to include more nutrients into your diet. It is a great source of protein, antioxidants, and healthy fats and is very filling.

Peanut butter is also moderately rich in vitamins and minerals:

- Vitamin E: 45% of the RDI (Reference Daily Intake)
- Vitamin B3 (Niacin): 67% of the RDI
- Vitamin B6: 27% of the RDI
- Folate: 18% of the RDI

Note: peanut butter can be unhealthy in large amounts and can cause harm. Small to moderate amounts can have a positive effect and are the better way to go (Is Peanut Butter Good or Bad for Your Health?).

 According to peanutbutterlovers.com, the average American consumes about 3 pounds of peanut butter each year!

Green Tea:

Green tea has been shown to improve blood flow and decrease cholesterol. A 2013 review of many studies found green tea helped prevent a range of heart-related issues, from congestive heart disease to high blood pressure. Green tea also contains catechins that lower cholesterol and blood pressure and also helps stabilize blood sugar for people with diabetes.

 Catechins are antioxidants that fight and may even prevent cell damage. Green tea is not processed much before it's poured into your cup, so it's rich in catechins.

Cashew:

Cashews are always welcome into good diets. They are rich in healthy fats, vitamins, and minerals. They are great for eye and blood health and weight loss. The healthy fats are great for helping you feel fuller for a longer period of time and can help reduce your risk of stroke and heart disease. Studies have also shown that eating nuts like cashews can be linked to cancer prevention (Are Cashews Good for You?).

One ounce of raw cashew contains:

- ❖ 157 calories
- ❖ 8.56 grams of carbohydrate
- ❖ 1.68 grams of sugar
- ❖ 0.9 grams of fiber
- ❖ 5.17 grams of protein

 Mobile Cuisine reports that cashews are in the same family as poison ivy and poison sumac, and thus why cashews are never sold in their shells.

Cinnamon:

Cinnamon is great in all sorts of ways. It is great for your health and it adds a very warm, spiced flavor to food. Cinnamon is rich in antioxidants, vitamins and substances that have medicinal properties. Cinnamon has anti-inflammatory properties while also promoting a fast metabolism. It also has a powerful effect against diabetes and can lower blood sugar levels (10 Evidence-Based Health Benefits of Cinnamon).

According to USDA 2.6 grams of cinnamon contains these elements among others:

- ❖ Energy: 6.42 calories
- ❖ Carbohydrates: 2.1 grams
- ❖ Calcium: 26.1 milligrams

 Cinnamon sticks are also called quills.

Chapter 8

21 Smoothie Recipes for a 21-Day Smoothie Challenge

Here are 21 smoothie recipes that my family and I really love. These smoothie recipes are great for helping improve your diet and helping incorporate more fruits, veggies, proteins, fats, and whole grains into your diet. Please feel free to tweak the recipes, measurements, and add your own twist to these smoothies if you want. Now, I'll leave you to discover these smoothies and hopefully try them out! Enjoy!!

Get a link to a free list of ingredients and tips for the next 7 days smoothie diet at www.diyasworld.com

1. Tropical Citrus Boost

Ingredients

- ½ cup pineapple
- 1/3 cup coconut milk
- ½ spoon flax/Chia seeds/Oxi-Blast powder
- ¾ cup freshly squeezed Orange Juice (OJ)
- ½ cup ice

Directions

- Add OJ and coconut milk into blender
- Add fruit, flax or chia seeds, and ice
- Blend until smooth
- Pour and serve

2. Sweet Green Machine

Ingredients

- ½ cup spinach
- ½ cup frozen mango
- ½ cup frozen pineapple
- 2/3 cup OJ
- ½ tsp flax seeds
- ½ cup ice

Directions

- Add OJ and ice into blender of choice
- Add fruit and vegetables
- Blend until smooth
- Add flax seeds and blend until smooth
- Pour and serve

3. Blueberry Cheesecake

Ingredients

- ❖ 15 cashews
- ❖ 1 cup frozen blueberries
- ❖ ¼ tsp chia seeds/Oxi-Blast
- ❖ ¼ tsp cinnamon
- ❖ ¼ cup heavy cream or 1 tbsp. cream cheese
- ❖ ¾ cup of any milk

Directions

- ❖ Add milk, cashews, and heavy cream/cream cheese
- ❖ Add chia, Oxi-Blast, blueberries and cinnamon
- ❖ Blend until smooth
- ❖ Pour and serve

4. Strawmango Lemonade

Ingredients

- ❖ 1 cup frozen strawberries
- ❖ ½ cup mango
- ❖ ¾ cup water
- ❖ Juice of ¼ lemon
- ❖ Natural sweetener (Ex. Agave, stevia)
  *Use according to your preference.

Directions

- ❖ Add water and lemon juice into blender of choice
- ❖ Add fruit and sweetener
- ❖ Blend until smooth
- ❖ Pour and serve

5. Chocolate Energy

Ingredients

- ❖ 4 squares (1 oz.) (70% cocoa) dark chocolate
- ❖ ¼ scoop chocolate protein powder (optional)
- ❖ 1 frozen banana
- ❖ 5-10 soaked cashews
- ❖ ½ cup cooled coffee
- ❖ ¼ cup milk (optional)
- ❖ ½ cup ice

Directions

- ❖ Add coffee and milk into blender
- ❖ Add rest of Ingredients
- ❖ Blend until smooth
- ❖ Pour and serve

6. Dream Green

Ingredients

- ❖ ½ cup frozen pineapple
- ❖ ½ cup peaches
- ❖ 1 kale leaf
- ❖ ¾ cup water
- ❖ ¼ cup ice

Directions

- ❖ Remove kale leaf from stem
- ❖ Add kale and water into blender
- ❖ Pulse until well incorporated
- ❖ Add fruit and ice
- ❖ Blend until smooth
- ❖ Pour and serve

7. Banana Surprise

Ingredients

- ❖ 1-2 frozen bananas
- ❖ ¾ cup milk
- ❖ 5-7 ice cubes
- ❖ ¼ tsp cinnamon
- ❖ ¼ tsp Oxi-Blast
- ❖ 2-4 dates

Directions

- ❖ Soak dates in hot water for 10 min
- ❖ Add all ingredients to blender
- ❖ Blend 20 sec
- ❖ Add rest of ingredients
- ❖ Blend for 40 sec
- ❖ Pour and serve

Get a comprehensive free list of ingredients and tips for the next 7 days smoothie diet at <u>www.diyasworld.com</u>

8. Berry Delight

Ingredients

- ½ cup frozen blueberries
- ½ cup frozen strawberries
- 1/3 cup raspberries
- 1/2 spoonful of Oxi-Blast
- 1 cup Orange Juice
- (Optional) 1 banana

Directions

- Pour OJ into blender
- Add berries and (if desired) banana
- Add Oxi-Blast
- Blend until smooth
- Pour and serve

9. Water Mango (My Favorite!!)

Ingredients

- ¾ cup watermelon
- ½ - 1 mango
- 5-7 ice cubes
- (Optional) 1 tsp lemon or lime juice

Directions

- Put all ingredients into blender except ice
- Blend until smooth
- Add ice into blender
- Blend again until smooth
- Pour and serve

10. Almond Blueberry

Ingredients

- ❖ 1 cup almond milk
- ❖ 2/3 cup frozen blueberries
- ❖ ½ banana
- ❖ ¼ tsp cinnamon and nutmeg
- ❖ 1 tsp chia seeds

Directions

- ❖ Put all ingredients, except chia seeds into blender
- ❖ Blend until smooth
- ❖ Pour, garnish with chia seeds, and serve

11. Cherry Berry Yogurt Smoothie (Mom's Favorite!)

Ingredients

- ❖ 6 pitted cherries
- ❖ ⅓ cup strawberries
- ❖ ¼ cup strawberry yogurt (or regular yogurt)
- ❖ 4 pitted dates
- ❖ 5-7 ice cubes

Directions

- ❖ Blend cherries, strawberries, dates and yogurt until smooth
- ❖ Add ice
- ❖ Blend again until smooth
- ❖ Pour and serve

Diya Nath ❖ 75

12. Avocado Berry Miracle

Ingredients

- ❖ 1 tsp coconut oil
- ❖ ¼ tsp cinnamon
- ❖ 1 cup frozen blueberries
- ❖ ¼ avocado
- ❖ ½ cup water
- ❖ 1 tsp chia seeds

Directions

- ❖ Add water first into blender
- ❖ Add berries, avocado, and cinnamon
- ❖ Blend until smooth
- ❖ Add oil and chia seeds
- ❖ Blend until smooth
- ❖ Pour and serve

13. Citrus Green Refresher

Ingredients

- 5-7 OJ ice cubes
  (*Freeze freshly-squeezed OJ to get OJ ice cubes)
- ½ cup OJ
- Juice of ¼ lemon
- ½ cup spinach

Directions

- First blend lemon juice, OJ and spinach until smooth
- Add OJ ice cubes
- Blend until smooth
- Pour and serve

Get a free comprehensive list of ingredients and tips for the next 7 days smoothie diet at www.diyasworld.com

14. Strawberry Orange Cool-Aid

Ingredients

- ¼ cup strawberries
- ½ tsp ginger
- ½ cup freshly-squeezed OJ and fresh oranges
- ½ cup ice

Directions

- Add berries, OJ, ginger and ice into blender
- Blend until smooth
- Pour and serve

15. "Potabolism" Boost

Ingredients

- ❖ 1 frozen banana
- ❖ ½ cup spinach
- ❖ ¼ scoop protein powder
- ❖ ¼ spoon Oxi-Blast
- ❖ ½ cup water
- ❖ ¼ tsp cinnamon

Directions

- ❖ Add all ingredients, except protein powder into blender
- ❖ Blend until smooth
- ❖ Add protein powder
- ❖ Blend until smooth, pour, garnish, and serve

16. Banana Berry Refresher

Ingredients

- ❖ ½ banana
- ❖ 5-7 frozen strawberries
- ❖ ½ cup blueberries (fresh or frozen)
- ❖ ½ cup milk
- ❖ ½ tsp Oxi-Blast

Directions

- ❖ Add all ingredients into blender
- ❖ Blend until smooth
- ❖ Pour and serve

17. Citrus Berry

Ingredients

- ½ cup frozen blueberries
- 6 OJ ice cubes
- ½ cup strawberries
- ½ cup water

Directions

- Add all ingredients into blender
- Blend until smooth
- Pour and serve

18. Rose Water Green

Ingredients

- ½ cup spinach
- ½ pear
- ½ cup water
- ½ cup pineapple
- ½ tsp rose water
- 1 tsp chia seeds/Oxi-Blast
- 1 spring parsley

Directions

- Blend all ingredients except chia seeds until smooth
- Add chia seeds
- Blend until smooth
- Pour and serve

19. Pina Colada

Ingredients

- 1 cup pineapple
- ¾ cup coconut milk
- ½ cup spinach
- 2 tsp shredded coconut (if you don't have coconut milk, or as a garnish)

Directions

- Add all ingredients into blender
- Blend until smooth
- Pour and serve

20. Blueberry Protein Shake

Ingredients

- ❖ ½ cup frozen blueberries
- ❖ 1 banana
- ❖ ½ cup milk
- ❖ ¼ scoop vanilla protein powder
- ❖ 1 tsp Oxi-Blast
- ❖ 10 almonds
- ❖ 1 tsp hemp hearts

Directions

- ❖ Add all ingredients, except protein powder and Oxi-Blast into blender
- ❖ Blend until smooth
- ❖ Add protein powder
- ❖ Blend until smooth
- ❖ Garnish with Oxi-Blast and pour and serve

21. Strawberry and Banana Flax Smoothie

Ingredients

- ½ cup strawberries
- 1 banana
- ½ cup milk or water
- 1 tsp ground flax seed
- ½ cup ice

Directions

- Add all ingredients into blender
- Blend until smooth
- Pour and serve

Chapter 9

Daily Routine for a Healthier You

❖ Drink a glass of warm water with a pinch of lemon juice and 1tbsp honey every morning on an empty stomach.

❖ Eat around 5-10 almonds soaked in water overnight after the glass of water (this is my grandma's secret recipe for brain food).

❖ Eat a healthy, filling breakfast with berries, oats and super-foods for energy.

❖ Try to avoid food filled with sugar and sugar substitutes like bagels, donuts, cakes and pastries. They might be saved for special treats.

❖ Complex carbohydrates like rice, pasta, bread and wheat should be avoided and substituted with more coarse, fiber-filled carbs like millet, barley, rye, quinoa, etc.

❖ Drink one 8-ounce glass of water every one-to-one and half hours. If you continue throughout the day, it will get you your 8 glasses of water requirement without you noticing it.

❖ Incorporate more vegetables and fruits in your diet. At least 6-7 servings daily.

- Have snacks that are filled with heart healthy nuts like walnuts, pistachios, almonds etc.
- Reduce the use of processed food like salami, hotdogs and sausages.
- Exercise at least 30 minutes for 5 days/week. This can be jogging, dancing, swimming, aerobic exercises, any kind of sports or even walking (whatever you prefer).
- Take time for yourself to do what you like best. I love reading and playing Overwatch.
- Don't forget to breathe. For 5 minutes twice a day, breathe in through the nose and breathe out through the mouth.

5 Tips for Storing Smoothies

The shelf life of a smoothie can be increased by preventing oxidation of the smoothie. These are some quick tricks you can do to enjoy your smoothie later:

1. Add ½ tsp of lemon juice, it will prevent oxidation and keep your smoothie fresh longer.
2. Leftover or extra smoothies can be filled to the brim of a glass container and sealed tight. Mason Jars work the best. Don't leave space for air. Put it in the refrigerator ASAP. Refrigerated smoothies should be consumed within 36 hours to retain their nutrients.
3. Glass jugs with lids work for storing large quantities.
4. You can also freeze them in the same mason jars for over 5-6 days.

5. If you store in a glass container, make sure to quickly give it a twirl before you drink it, as sometimes the smoothie tends to settle.

TIP: To pack smoothies for kids and for yourself for lunch, keep the empty thermos in the fridge overnight and then add the smoothie in the morning just before leaving home.

Sweet treats you can make from Smoothies

If you want to develop a healthy eating habit, and you are worried about sugar intake by eating candies, chocolates, desserts, etc., but you still have a sweet tooth and want those extra sweet treats at the end of the day, you can do the following:

1. Use an ice tray and freeze some of the smoothie to make smoothie cubes that you can relish later.
2. Make popsicles out of smoothies.
3. Make a smoothie bowl and store it for about 3 hours and have a quick snack.

Suggested readings

❖ *Nuritbullet Recipes* by Stephanie Shaw
❖ *Blend Your Way to Bliss* by Adam Collins
❖ *Juicing and Pulp Recipes* by Tracee Sloan
❖ *Green Smoothie Habit* by Jane Haddad
❖ *The Reboot with Joe* by Joe Cross
❖ *Green for Life* by Victoria Boutenko

Praises for the Book

It is truly amazing that Diya has created this masterpiece, created a product for reducing stress and antioxidants (Oxi-Blast®) and is also a classical vocalist and violinist all at only 14 years of age. Her compassion towards the needy and her strive to equity and justice through her Discord server, SPEAK (Support, Positivity, Equality, Acceptance/Assistance and Kindness) is very humbling. She always strives to give comfort to others and hence ends up getting everyone's love in return. I wish her unsurpassable amount of love and best wishes.

Pandit Tarun BhattacharyaGlobal Ambassador of music, Santoor Maestro, Sangeet Natak Academy and Sangeet Maha Sanmaan Awardee, India

"As an entrepreneur, minority business owner, and business coach, I am in awe of Diya's boundless optimism and intellect. It is not the norm to have a person as young as Diya take charge of her diagnosis and research nutritional solutions that require a change in how one interacts with their food. Diya is committed to adopting healthy habits for a better quality of life and has found the best way to share her philosophies and recipes with the world. I am so proud of Diya and love her healthy, tasty juice recipes."

**Diana White
CEO, Chandler Innovations**

In an age where we want everything fast and we want it easy, Diya Nath, masterfully combines both to provide some of the most creative and appealing solutions to a personal health and wellness challenge faced by countless teens and adults. Diya infuses humor, personality, research, and carefully crafted recipes to offer readers an inspiring view into her world as an ambitious teen who's on a mission to bring about change in a unique way—by working to change youth from the inside. Read on, and receive from Diya, self-proclaimed health advocate for younger generations, a heaping tablespoon of passion and an open reservation for any day of the week to enjoy her culinary creations.

**Bridgett McGowen-Hawkins, International
Professional Speaker, Author, and Publisher**

I am very impressed by this talented young lady. She has done her research scientifically and has come up with amazing smoothie recipes which are both healthy and tasty. She has included superfoods and antioxidant rich foods that I recommend to my patients all the time as a medical professional. I have tried most of the smoothies and must say that they make me feel fresh and energetic. I hope Diya Nath continues to enchant us with more mouthwatering recipes in future.

**Dr Gayatri Majumdar, MBBS,
FRACP (Geriatrician), Sydney, NSW, Australia**

I am so thrilled to see the book and research Diya had put in her book. I use her tasty smoothy recipes in my retreats and in my summer camps. It is such a privilege for me to meet such an intellectual and a fighter who wants to serve the community with her lessons and challenges. She is such an inspiration to the present generation. I wish her so much luck on her future endeavors that she keeps following her heart and bring the treasures like 'Healthy habits for healthier you' to the world.

Durga Mamidipalli
Spiritual coach and Trauma specialist

A small little book covering the story of a fighter kid who is not only determined to solve her problems but also shares all her research with others too for their greater health. The basic information about proteins, carbs, and vitamins is I think the most essential part for everyone to know as a life skill to take care of their health and food.

Sourabh Goyal Founder, The Goalchy
Club Community, 3Catalyst Partner

As a future culinary gastronomist, not only did Diya research for her own health's benefit, but she also shared her findings to help others. Personally, this book blessed me in that I am prescribed one of the medicines referenced in Diya's research and because of her amazing ability to simplify the science of it all, I can now make the mind shift of becoming a healthier version of myself and making better dietary choices for me and my family. Amazing job, Diya! I can't wait for Oxi-Blast® to hit the market and take off!

Tameka Chapman, DTM #1 Bestselling Author,
Award-Winning Motivational Speaker
& Perseverance Mindset Coach

"I am so happy that now we have "Healthy Habits for a Healthier You" by Diya Nath, one of the youngest proponents of smoothies. She is in true sense a health advocate for the younger generation. Her book is a perfect blend of science and art of smoothie making. It is my honor to introduce this book to you that will help you elevate your health and well being no matter the age."

Parul Agrawal Bestselling Author,
TEDxSpeaker, Publisher

Throughout my editing career I have often worked on wellness guides and wellness articles. As my husband has a functional medicine clinic, I am quite experienced with alternative health medicine, supplements and of course juicing and detox cleanses. When I was asked to edit Diya's smoothie guide, I was pleasantly surprised to find it was unique, informative and contained different recipes from the usual smoothie guides. It is amazing that this was written by a 14-year-old; I can tell that Diya will go far and her book exudes her passion. It is reassuring to know that there are teenagers like her coming along; after all, they are the next leading generation! I am eagerly awaiting the juicing guide which I'm hoping will follow soon!

Heidi De LoveFreelance Editor, Editor of # 1 Bestseller
ONE, Communication Consultant & Content Writer

Glossary

A

Amlodipine - 12

B

Blender - vii, xi-xiii, 3 27-30, 55, 57, 60, 63, 65-66, 68, 71, 73, 76, 81, 84, 87, 90, 92, 95,

Bran - 16, 27

D

Diabetes - 5, 11-14, 16-17, 45, 49, 51, 109

E

Endosperm - 16

G

Germ - 16

GI (gastrointestinal) - 10

Gut Microbiome - 9-11, 14

H

Hypertension - 12-14

L

LB (Laura Bertani) Broth

Losartan - 12

K

K-12

M

Metformin -5, 12

P

PD (Parkinson's disease) - 9-10

S

Saturated Fat - 15

Smoothie - v, xi, xii-xiii, 1-4, 7-8, 14, 20-21, 24-31, 40, 47, 52, 67, 74, 80, 95, 97-98, 100, 102-104

Superfood - viii, 7, 22, 25-26, 42, 96, 108, 111

U

Unsaturated Fat - 15

References

1. "Acanthosis Nigricans - Symptoms and Causes." Mayo Clinic, 24 Apr. 2018, www.mayoclinic.org/diseases-conditions/acanthosis-nigricans/symptoms-causes/syc-20368983.

1. "14 Things You Didn't Know About Strawberries." Food Republic, 20 May 2013, www.foodrepublic.com/2013/05/20/14-things-you-didnt-know-about-strawberries/.

2. "FoodData Central." fdc.nal.usda.gov/.

3. "Green Tea Health Benefits." WebMD, 23 Sept. 2013, www.webmd.com/food-recipes/features/health-benefits-of-green-tea#1.

4. "Increased Anthocyanin and Flavonoids in Mango Fruit Peel Are Associated with Cold and Pathogen Resistance." ScienceDirect.com | Science, Health and Medical Journals, Full Text Articles and Books,

5. "Technical Advance: Ascorbic Acid Induces Development of Double-positive T Cells from Human Hematopoietic Stem Cells in the Absence of Stromal Cells. - PubMed - NCBI." National Center for Biotechnology Information, www.ncbi.nlm.nih.gov/pubmed/25157026.

6. "10 Health Benefits of Spirulina." Healthline, Healthline Media, 5 Oct. 2018, www.healthline.com/nutrition/10-proven-benefits-of-spirulina. Accessed 22 Oct. 2019.

7. "Should You Peel Your Fruits and Vegetables?" Healthline, Healthline Media, 9 Dec. 2017, www.healthline.com/nutrition/peeling-fruits-veggies#section2.

8. "6 Good Reasons to Eat a Banana Today." Healthxchange. Sg, 2019, www.healthxchange.sg/food-nutrition/food-tips/good-reasons-eat-banana-today.

9. "7 Goji Berry Benefits Backed by Science." Www. Medicalnewstoday.Com, www.medicalnewstoday.com/articles/322693.

10. "7 Science-Based Health Benefits of Drinking Enough Water." Healthline, 2017, www.healthline.com/nutrition/7-health-benefits-of-water.

11. "8 Impressive Health Benefits of Pineapple." Healthline, 2018, www.healthline.com/nutrition/benefits-of-pineapple.

12. "9 Legitimate Health Benefits of Eating Whole Grains." Healthline, 2016, www.healthline.com/nutrition/9-benefits-of-whole-grains.

13. "Chia Seeds: Health Benefits and Recipe Tips." Www. Medicalnewstoday.Com, www.medicalnewstoday.com/articles/291334.

14. "Consumer Health: Acai Berries — Superfood or Hype?" Https://Newsnetwork.Mayoclinic.Org/ , newsnetwork. mayoclinic.org/discussion/consumer-health-acai-berries-superfood-or-hype/. Accessed 29 Apr. 2020.

15. "Dietary Fats." Www.Heart.Org, 2010, www.heart.org/en/healthy-living/healthy-eating/eat-smart/fats/dietary-fats.

16. "Is Peanut Butter Bad for You, or Good? A Look at the Evidence." Healthline, www.healthline.com/nutrition/is-peanut-butter-bad-for-you.

17. "Just Fun Facts | Fun and Interesting Site." Justfunfacts. Com, 2019, justfunfacts.com.

18. "Oranges: Health Benefits, Nutrition, Diet, and Risks." Www.Medicalnewstoday.Com, www.medicalnewstoday. com/articles/272782#benefits.

19. "Simple Steps to Preventing Diabetes." The Nutrition Source, 25 July 2016, www.hsph.harvard.edu/ nutritionsource/disease-prevention/diabetes-prevention/ preventing-diabetes-full-story/.

20. "Slide Show: Add Antioxidants to Your Diet." Mayo Clinic, 2017, www.mayoclinic.org/healthy-lifestyle/nutrition-and-healthy-eating/multimedia/antioxidants/sls-20076428.

21. "The Importance of Protein in Your Diet." Detour Bar, 2016, www.detourbar.com/pages/the-importance-of-protein-in-your-diet.

22. "Top 10 Health Benefits of Flax Seeds." Healthline, www.healthline.com/nutrition/benefits-of-flaxseeds.

23. "What Are the Key Functions of Carbohydrates?" Healthline, 2017, www.healthline.com/nutrition/ carbohydrate-functions.

24. Adda Bjarnad ó ttir, MS, LN. "6 Evidence-Based Health Benefits of Hemp Seeds." Healthline, Healthline Media, 11 Sept. 2018, www.healthline.com/nutrition/6-health-benefits-of-hemp-seeds.

25. Bauer, Brent. "The Microbiome and Gastrointestinal Disorders From Mayo Clinic | Thorne." www.thorne. com, 11 Sept. 2019, www.thorne.com/take-5-daily/article/ your-gut-your-health-the-microbiome-and-gastrointestinal-disorders. Accessed 29 Apr. 2020.

26. Beil, Laura. "A Gut-Brain Link for Parkinson's Gets a Closer Look." Science News, 7 Dec. 2018, www.sciencenews.org/ article/parkinsons-disease-gut-microbes-brain-link. Accessed 29 Apr. 2020.

27. Blumberg, Perri O. "7 Healthy Smoothies Nutritionists Swear By." SELF, www.self.com/gallery/weight-loss-smoothies-nutritionists-swear-by.

28. Carr AC and Maggini S. "Vitamin C and Immune Function. - PubMed - NCBI." National Center for Biotechnology Information, www.ncbi.nlm.nih.gov/pubmed/29099763.

29. Chandran B and Goel A. "A Randomized, Pilot Study to Assess the Efficacy and Safety of Curcumin in Patients with Active Rheumatoid Arthritis. - PubMed - NCBI." National Center for Biotechnology Information, www.ncbi.nlm.nih.gov/pubmed/22407780.

30. Chen XM, et al. "Flavonoid Composition of Orange Peel and Its Association with Antioxidant and Anti-inflammatory Activities. - PubMed - NCBI." National Center for Biotechnology Information, www.ncbi.nlm.nih.gov/pubmed/27719891.

31. Coussens LM and Werb Z. "Inflammation and Cancer. - PubMed - NCBI." National Center for Biotechnology Information, www.ncbi.nlm.nih.gov/pubmed/12490959.

32. Cui H , et al. "Oxidative Stress, Mitochondrial Dysfunction, and Aging. - PubMed - NCBI." National Center for Biotechnology Information, www.ncbi.nlm.nih.gov/pubmed/21977319.

33. "E. coli May Hold One of the Keys to Treating Parkinson's." (n.d.). Retrieved fromhttps://www.infectioncontroltoday.com/bacterial/e-coli-may-hold-one-keys-treating-parkinsons

34. Enterotoxigenic E. coli (ETEC) | E. coli | CDC. (2019, January 14). Retrieved fromhttps://www.cdc.gov/ecoli/etec.html

35. Escherichia coli (a.k.a. E. coli). (2015, March 11). Retrieved fromhttps://www.gutmicrobiotaforhealth.com/en/glossary/escherichia-coli-a-k-a-e-coli/

36. Fanous, Summer. "Are Cashews Good for You?" Healthline, www.healthline.com/health/are-cashews-good-for-you.

37. Finer, Alex. "13 Essential Vitamins Your Body Needs to Stay Healthy." Reader's Digest, Reader's Digest, 20 June 2018, www.readersdigest.ca/health/healthy-living/13-essential-vitamins-your-body-needs-stay-healthy/.

38. Groves, Melissa. "Red Raspberries: Nutrition Facts, Benefits and More." Healthline, 3 Oct. 2018, www.healthline.com/nutrition/raspberry-nutrition. Accessed 7 May 2020.

39. Gunnars, Kris. "11 Proven Health Benefits of Chia Seeds." Healthline, 8 Aug. 2018, www.healthline.com/nutrition/11-proven-health-benefits-of-chia-seeds#section11. Accessed 7 May 2020.

40. Hanson, Carl. "How To Make A Smoothie To Replace A Meal." Allrecipes, www.allrecipes.com/article/drink-your-breakfast/.

41. helpguidewp. "HelpGuide.Org." HelpGuide.Org, 26 June 2019, www.helpguide.org/harvard/vitamins-and-minerals.htm.

42. https://www.facebook.com/begoodorganics. "Cacao: 5 Little Known Benefits of This Amazonian Superfood - Be Good Organics." Be Good Organics, 6 July 2013, begoodorganics.com/cacao-5-little-known-benefits-of-this-amazonian-superfood/.

43. Huijskens MJ, et al. "Technical Advance: Ascorbic Acid Induces Development of Double-positive T Cells from Human Hematopoietic Stem Cells in the Absence of Stromal Cells. - PubMed - NCBI." National Center for Biotechnology Information, www.ncbi.nlm.nih.gov/pubmed/25157026.

44. Jennings, Kerri-Ann. "Top 9 Health Benefits of Eating Watermelon." Healthline, 9 Aug. 2017, www.healthline.com/nutrition/watermelon-health-benefits#section8. Accessed 6 May 2020.
45. Kris Gunnars, BSc. "4 Natural Supplements That Are As Powerful As Drugs." Healthline, www.healthline.com/nutrition/4-supplements-as-powerful-as-drugs.
46. Kubala, Jillian. "7 Impressive Health Benefits of Cherries." Healthline, Healthline Media, 19 June 2019, www.healthline.com/nutrition/cherries-benefits.
47. Lauricella M, et al. "Multifaceted Health Benefits of Mangifera Indica L. (Mango): The Inestimable Value of Orchards Recently Planted in Sicilian Rural Areas. - PubMed - NCBI." National Center for Biotechnology Information, www.ncbi.nlm.nih.gov/pubmed/28531110.
48. Leech, Joe. "10 Evidence-Based Health Benefits of Cinnamon." Healthline, 5 July 2018, healthline.com/nutrition/10-proven-benefits-of-cinnamon#section6. Accessed 7 May 2020.
49. Leech, Joe. "10 Proven Health Benefits of Blueberries." Healthline, 9 Oct. 2018, www.healthline.com/nutrition/10-proven-benefits-of-blueberries. Accessed 7 May 2020.
50. Liguori I, et al. "Oxidative Stress, Aging, and Diseases. - PubMed - NCBI." National Center for Biotechnology Information, www.ncbi.nlm.nih.gov/pubmed/29731617.
51. Maggini S, et al. "Selected Vitamins and Trace Elements Support Immune Function by Strengthening Epithelial Barriers and Cellular and Humoral Immune Responses. - PubMed - NCBI." National Center for Biotechnology Information, www.ncbi.nlm.nih.gov/pubmed/17922955.

52. McDonell, Kayla. "How Much Fruit Should You Eat per Day?" Healthline, Healthline Media, 25 Mar. 2017, www.healthline.com/nutrition/how-much-fruit-per-day.

53. McNamara, Patrick. "Learn About the Gastrointestinal Effects of Parkinson's Disease." Verywell Health, 27 Nov. 2019, www.verywellhealth.com/the-gastrointestinal-effects-of-parkinsons-disease-2612184. Accessed 29 Apr. 2020.

54. Moylan JS and Reid MB. "Oxidative Stress, Chronic Disease, and Muscle Wasting. - PubMed - NCBI." National Center for Biotechnology Information, www.ncbi.nlm.nih.gov/pubmed/17266144.

55. Neurodegenerative Diseases. (n.d.). Retrieved from https://www.niehs.nih.gov/research/supported/health/neurodegenerative/index.cfm

56. P, Libby. "Inflammation in Atherosclerosis. - PubMed - NCBI." National Center for Biotechnology Information, www.ncbi.nlm.nih.gov/pubmed/12490960.

57. Parkinson's Disease Statistics. (2017, May 31). Retrieved from https://parkinsonsnewstoday.com/parkinsons-disease-statistics/

58. Petre, Alina. "10 Surprising Health Benefits and Uses of Peaches." Healthline, Healthline Media, 17 Jan. 2019, www.healthline.com/nutrition/peach-fruit-benefits.

59. Ross, R. (2019, January 7). What Is E. Coli? Retrieved from https://www.livescience.com/64436-e-coli.html

60. Takada Y, et al. "Nonsteroidal Anti-inflammatory Agents Differ in Their Ability to Suppress NF-kappaB Activation, Inhibition of Expression of Cyclooxygenase-2 and Cy... - PubMed - NCBI." National Center for Biotechnology Information, www.ncbi.nlm.nih.gov/pubmed/15489888.

61. Tan, Verena. "Top 10 Health Benefits of Flax Seeds." Healthline, 26 Apr. 2017, www.healthline.com/nutrition/benefits-of-flaxseeds#section3. Accessed 7 May 2020.

62. The role of microbial amyloid in neurodegeneration. (2017, December 21). Retrieved from https://journals.plos.org/plospathogens/article?id=10.1371/journal.ppat.1006654

63. The unexhausted potential of E. coli. (n.d.). Retrieved from https://www.ncbi.nlm.nih.gov/pmc/articles/PMC4373459/

64. Tjernberg LO, Rising A, Johansson J, Jaudzems K, Westermark P. Transmis Why? (2014, July 17). Retrieved from https://www.neurodegenerationresearch.eu/about/why/

65. Walker LC, Schelle J, Jucker M. The Prion-Like Properties of Amyloid-beta Assemblies: Implications for Alzheimer's disease. Cold Spring Harbor Perspectives in Medicine. 2016; 6(7). Pmid: 27270558.

66. Walker LC, Schelle J, Jucker M. The Prion-Like Properties of Amyloid-beta Assemblies: Implications for Alzheimer's Disease. Cold Spring HarbPerspect Med. 2016; 6(7). Pmid:27270558. sible amyloid. J Intern Med. 2016; 280(2):153–63. Pmid: 27002185.

67. Whelan, Corey. "Everything You Need to Know About the Fruitarian Diet." Healthline, Healthline Media, 19 July 2017, www.healthline.com/health/food-nutrition/fruit-diet.

68. Zhang YJ, Li S, Gan RY, et al. Impact bacteria on human health and diseases. Int J Mol Sci. 2015; 16(4):7493–7519.

Made in the USA
Coppell, TX
07 September 2020